A Manual
for
Translators
of
Mathematical Russian

by

S. H. Gould

Published by the
American Mathematical Society
Providence, Rhode Island
1966

A Manual for Translators of Mathematical Russian

by

S. H. Gould

Published by the
American Mathematical Society
Providence, Rhode Island
1966

TABLE OF CONTENTS

INTRODUCTION 1

Part One. GENERAL REMARKS ON GRAMMAR AND STYLE ... 3
1. abstract nouns 3
2. acknowledgments 3
3. adjectives (two or more) 4
4. adverbs as syntax carriers 5
5. dangling gerunds (participles) 5
6. dash 7
7. double negatives 8
8. genitive after a negative verb 8
9. nouns followed by cases other than the genitive 9
10. order of subject and object 9
11. participles as "slight" words 10
12. prepositional phrases 11
13. repetition of words 12
14. sentence connection 13
15. separation of symbols 13
16. separation of verb and object 14
17. singulars and plurals 15
18. slight words 16
19. symbols as syntax carriers 18
20. symbols in the genitive case 19
21. verbal adjectives (passive) 20

Part Two. RUSSIAN WORDS AND PHRASES 22
1. большой 22
2. должно 22
3. если же 23
4. замена 23
5. и 23
6. каково бы ни было 24

iii

TABLE OF CONTENTS

7. ли 24
8. называть 25
9. некоторый 26
10. обозначить 27
11. общий 27
12. по 27
13. пока, пока не 28
14. пункт 29
15. работа 29
16. тот или иной 29
17. уже 30

Part Three. ENGLISH WORDS AND PHRASES 31
1. "a" or "the"? 31
2. and 31
3. anomalous use of "if" 32
4. both 33
5. "can" and "may" 34
6. if and only if 35
7. it 35
8. -ly words 36
9. respectively 37
10. since ..., then 37
11. such that 38
12. "the" instead of "this" or "that" 38
13. whose 39

Part Four. PREPARATION OF THE TYPEWRITTEN
MANUSCRIPT 41

INTRODUCTION

A good translator of scientific Russian must have three quali-
fications. In sharply increasing order of importance, these qualifi-
cations are:
  i)   knowledge of Russian
  ii) knowledge of English
  iii) expert knowledge of some branch of science.
Thus the best translators of mathematical Russian are compe-
tent mathematicians whose native language is English and whose
knowledge of Russian, in some cases at least, has been somewhat
hastily acquired. During the past four years the writer of the present booklet, in the course of editing more than 20,000 pages of
text, has kept a record of certain undesirable features, chiefly of
a grammatical or stylistic kind, to be found in some of the transla-
tions. The booklet is written in the hope that such features can
easily be eliminated, once they are pointed out.

If any translator, or would-be translator, feels that he himself
would never make any of the mistakes listed here let him be as-
sured that they are all taken from actual practice; and if, on the
other hand, he feels that some of the suggested improvements are
rather trivial, let him remember that irregular word-order or syntax,
under the influence of the idiom of the original language, is very
apt to occur in a translation and will cause the reader to stop and
ask himself, perhaps subconsciously, "how is that again?" When-
ever this happens the translation is not as good as it should be.

The essential part of the booklet consists of examples of the
kinds of mistakes often made. The Russian text is given first,
then the faulty translation (sometimes omitted and, if present, en-
closed in braces), then a suggested translation, and finally some
comments.

An unclassified list of examples would be of little value in
itself; no two passages are exactly alike and the translator must
recognize not the individual pitfall, but the species to which it
belongs. Thus an attempt has been made to put the comments in
such a form that they will be of general interest. In spite of the
fact that the examples are taken from mathematical literature, the
material should be interesting not only to mathematicians but to

physicists, chemists, engineers and others concerned with the translation of Russian science into English.

The manual is intended, not to teach beginners, but to assist
mathematicians already fairly well acquainted with Russian; it is
neither complete nor systematic, although the points discussed
here are representative of all the mistakes usually made; nor does
it discuss the problem of finding the technically correct translation
for a Russian mathematical term. Mathematicians who are looking
for information on this problem should consult the *Russian-English
Dictionary of the Mathematical Sciences* by A. J. Lohwater, published by the American Mathematical Society in 1961; and if they
are looking for systematic instruction in Russian grammar, express-
ly adapted to their needs, they are referred to the *Short Grammar
of the Russian Language* prefixed to that dictionary.

One indispensable rule for all good translation is that the
translator must read his work again at least twenty-four hours
later. At the time of first making a translation the translator knows
what his English sentences mean, since he has the Russian in
front of him (or in his memory) to tell him, and this unfair advantage over the ultimate consumer cannot be sufficiently discounted
in less than about twenty-four hours. Many examples will be found
below.

Part One

GENERAL REMARKS ON GRAMMAR AND STYLE

§1. ABSTRACT NOUNS

1. отсюда следует непустота множеств

   {hence follows the nonemptiness of the sets}

   it follows that the sets are not empty

2. ответить на вопрос о совпадении идеалов можно
   лишь при дальнейшем изучении многочленов

   {the answer to the question concerning the coinci-
   dence of the ideals is possible only after further
   study of the polynomials}

   to determine whether these ideals coincide we must
   make a further study of the polynomials

3. это уравнение противоречит допущению о наличии
   в области G точек, не принадлежащих области D

   {this equation contradicts the assumption concerning
   the presence in the domain G of points not belonging to the domain D}

   this equation contradicts the assumption that G contains points not belonging to D

Some of the numerous abstract nouns in present-day mathematical Russian (e.g. единственность = uniqueness) can be translated by the corresponding English noun, but most of them should
receive some other treatment. One objection, among many, to
translating abstract nouns by abstract nouns is that in an uninflected language like English the result is usually an unpleasant
pile-up of prepositional phrases.

§2. ACKNOWLEDGMENTS

1. приношу глубокую благодарность О. А. Олейник
   за полезные советы и внимание к работе

3

{I express deep gratitude to O. A. Oleĭnik for his
useful advices and attention to the work}

I wish to express gratitude to O. A. Oleĭnik for her
valuable advice and her interest in my work

2. считаю своим долгом выразить благодарность
профессору за постановку ряда задач

{I suppose it is my duty to express gratitude to my
professor, who has posed a number of problems}

I wish to express gratitude to my professor, who
formulated several of the problems

There are several pitfalls in the acknowledgments in scientific books or articles; here are three of them.

While few translators will write "advices" for the Russian
plural советы, many will make the same mistake with other words;
e.g. обозначения is "notation," not "notations,"

From the appearance of a surname in Russian it is generally
easy to tell whether it refers to a man or a woman, but names like
Oleĭnik and Bari (originating in non-Russian parts of the USSR)
show that care is needed. A woman's surname, if it is of non-Russian origin, is not inflected. For example, "with Mr. Truman" is
с господином Труманом, but "with Mrs. Truman" is с госпожой
Труман.

Polite expressions are notoriously dangerous; e.g. считаю
своим долгом cannot be translated by "I suppose it is my duty."

§3. ADJECTIVES (TWO OR MORE)

1. решение дифференциального линейного уравнения

{the solution of a differential linear equation ... }

the solution of a linear differential equation ...

2. пусть замкнутая жорданова спрямлемая кривая...

{let the closed Jordan rectifiable curve ... }

let the closed rectifiable Jordan curve ...

When two or more adjectives modify the same noun, the wordorder is freer in Russian than in English; e.g. "linear differential
equation" and "differential linear equation" seem to be almost

equally acceptable. In English the word-order is usually fixed (compare "a kind old man" with "an old kind man"), the rule being that the adjective more closely associated in meaning with the noun goes next to it. But often the accepted word-order seems to be only a matter of custom and in view of the fact that the "wrong" choice will have a surprisingly unpleasant effect, the translator should listen for it mentally in his twenty-four hour reread.

§4. ADVERBS AS SYNTAX CARRIERS

1. оценка (26) устанавливается вполне аналогично оценке (25)

   {the estimate (26) is set up completely analogously to the estimate (25)}

   the proof of (26) is completely analogous to that of (25).

2. но тогда от этих x, y можно было бы перейти к еще меньшим параллельно переходу от x_1, y_1 к x_2, y_2

   {but then from these x, y it would be possible to pass to still smaller parallelly to the passage from x_1, y_1 to x_2, y_2}

   but then we could proceed from the pair x, y to a still smaller pair in the same way as from x_1, y_1, to x_2, y_2

In Russian an adverb inherits more syntactical possibilities from its parent adjective than in English. In fact syntactically speaking, the English adverb is a poor relation; we may say "this proof is similar to that proof," but not "this theorem is proved similarly to that theorem." The three adverbs that cause the most difficulty are: аналогично = analogously, подобно = similarly, and параллельно = parallelly (?).

§5. DANGLING GERUNDS (PARTICIPLES)

1. следуя рассуждениям Н. Н. Баутина, теперь легко установить, что

{following the argument of N. N. Bautin, it is now easy to show that ... }

..., we can now easily show that ...

2. построение таких функций легко провести, несколько видоизменив метод, изложенный в (7)

{slightly changing the method explained in (7), the construction of such functions is easily carried out}

by a slight change in the method of (7) ...

In an inflected language like Russian, where a participle must agree in gender, number and case with the noun it modifies, a dangling participle is an extreme rarity. But the Russians also have their gerunds, следуя, читав, читавши, прочитав, прочитавши, which look to an English reader like active participles. Since such a form, in contrast to the true participles, is not inflected, it is not felt by the Russians to be a modifier of any particular word, and thus it can be used in a way which to an English reader looks like a dangling participle.

With respect to dangling participles in English there is a pronounced difference of opinion, leading at times to acrimony. Some hold that modern grammar, like modern music or art, must break out of the old forms if it is to achieve vivid expressiveness; while others, among them the present writer, hold that a dangling participle is simply a solecism, and the writers of the American Mathematical Society *Manual for Authors* express even more emphatic disapproval.

Concerning this controversy it should first be pointed out that a translation of a mathematical text is not a suitable proving-ground for experiments in art. Even admitting, what is not in fact the case, that the construction with a dangling participle is as perspicuous as any other, there remains a further requisite (the one referred to in the introduction as necessitating a twenty-four hour reread): the reader should be left free (this is the purpose of all grammar) to think about the meaning of the text, not about its grammatical structure; he should not be led into subconsciously expecting a certain grammatical feature and then stumbling with a shock, slight or otherwise, into something else. When he sees a participle, he will usually expect it to be supported later by a noun or pronoun. In example 2, the word "changing" brings into his mind the set of mathematicians "we" (including at least the author and himself) who have been active throughout the earlier part of the paragraph, and the habits of a lifetime cause him to feel at least a slight tremor when the word "we" fails to turn up. The essence of good style consists in not creating these tremors. Many idiomatic expressions in English involve what looks like, and perhaps in some cases actually is, a dangling participle: e.g. "including," "assuming that," "provided that," to mention only some of the ones used above. These expressions are unobjectionable, provided they do not lead the reader to expect a supporting noun, and they are becoming more numerous in English; but they are still a long way from including a phrase like "differentiating both sides, the equation becomes ...," and a mathematical text is not the place for a crusade on their behalf.

§6. DASH

1. обозначим через C пополнение S по этой норме и через C^* — соответствующее сопряженное пространство

   let us denote by C the completion of S in this norm and by C^* the corresponding conjugate space

2. функции L, M удовлетворяют условиям, описанным в теореме 5, ·а A, B, C —условиям гладкости

   {the functions L, M satisfy the conditions described in Theorem 5, but A, B, C —the conditions of smoothness}

   the functions L and M satisfy the conditions of Theorem 5, and A, B and C satisfy the smoothness conditions

3. продолжаемые решения обладают свойством II —свойством равномерной непрерывности

   the extended solutions have the property II, namely of uniform continuity

It is often stated that the Russian dash should be translated by "is" or "are," and in fact this translation is sometimes a good one; but in practice many translators simply replace the dash in Russian by a dash in English, which is seldom good. The above examples illustrate three frequent possibilities: simply omit the dash; repeat the word represented by the dash; and translate the dash by "namely."

§7. DOUBLE NEGATIVES

1. подгруппа P_n не содержится в централизаторе ни одного элемента группы B ...

the subgroup P_n is not contained in the centralizer of any non-unit element in B

2. пусть Z_j^p—p-мерные циклы, никакая линейная комбинация которых не гомологична нулю

let Z_j^p be p-dimensional cycles, no linear combination of which is homologous to zero

3. если многообразие M таково, что $A \neq B$ ни для каких S, то многообразие M эквивалентно многообразию N

if the manifold M is such that $A \neq B$ for every S, then M is equivalent to N

Double negatives often cause trouble, but the situation is really very simple. They are somewhat more common in Russian than in English (for an illustration of this fact see under "can and may" in §3) but, with the single exception noted below, they are used in exactly the same way in both languages; i.e. one negative cancels the other. Thus Turgenev's famous sentence нельзя верить, что такой язык не был дан великому народу means "it is impossible to believe that such a language was not given to a great people." The single exception is that when ни is used in a sentence containing the simple negative не (not), expressed or implied, the ни reinforces the meaning of the не. In example 3 above, the не is implied by the sign of inequality.

§8. GENITIVE AFTER A NEGATIVE VERB

1. если дуга не пересекает хорды

{if the arc does not intersect the chords}

if the arc does not intersect the chord

If a translator, in his haste, forgets that a negative verb is
followed by the genitive (partitive in origin; i.e. the arc does not
intersect any part of the chord) he is liable to make mistakes of
various kinds, such as confusing singulars with plurals.

§9. NOUNS FOLLOWED BY
CASES OTHER THAN THE GENITIVE

1. управление процессом передается этому элементу

   {the control is transferred by the process to this
   element}

   the control of the process is transferred to this
   element

Most Russian verbs govern the accusative case: thus обоб-
щать процесс (to generalize the process), and the corresponding
noun is followed by the genitive case: обобщение процесса
(generalization of the process). But many verbs govern some other
case e.g. the instrumental: thus управлять процессом (to control
the process, and then the corresponding noun is also followed by
this case (to be translated with "of" in English): thus управление процессом (control of the process).

§10. ORDER OF SUBJECT AND OBJECT

1. более тонкое необходимое условие дает касатель-
   ный пучок многообразия

   {a sharper necessary condition provides the tangent
   bundle of the manifold}

   the tangent bundle of the manifold provides a sharper
   necessary condition

Ordinarily a Russian writer has greater freedom of word-order
than his English counterpart because the subject and the object
will be distinguished by their case-endings. Thus "the dog sees
the cat" may be written either собака видит кошку or кошку
видит собака. But sometimes the Russians carry this freedom
too far; e.g. what is the meaning of мать любит дочь? In such
cases the translator must be on the alert, since the English word-
order may, or may not be misleading.

§11. PARTICIPLES AS "SLIGHT" WORDS

1. прежде всего мы установим необходимость сформулированного нами условия

   {first of all we shall establish the necessity of the condition formulated by us}

   we first establish the necessity of the condition

2. в первом пункте проводимого нами доказательства ...

   {in the first point of the proof being carried out by us ...}

   in the first section of this proof ...

3. если исключить указанные возможности

   {if we exclude the indicated possibilities, ...}

   except for these possibilities ...

4. по этой причине в разбираемом случае ...

   {for this reason in the analyzed case ...}

   thus in the case in question ...

5. будем говорить, что реперы выбраны канонизированными

   we shall say that the chosen frames of reference are canonical

6. связанный с этой функцией в (61) многочлен $R(t) \neq 0$ почти везде

   {the connected with this function in (61) polynomial $R(t) \neq 0$ almost everywhere}

   the polynomial, call it $R(t)$, corresponding to this function by (61), is almost everywhere nonzero

One of the numerous effects of the absence, in Russian, of a definite article is the superfluity, to English ears, of participles of all kinds, active and passive, present and past, preceding and following the noun. Very often the sole purpose of the Russian participle is to refer unambiguously to some preceding word, a task ideally performed by the English word "the."

When used in this way the participles come under the heading of "slight words" (see Section Two below) and are overtranslated by English participles. Often the best procedure is to omit the participle entirely; i.e., to translate it by the word "the," which will have to be used in any case.

If "the" does not seem to be enough, various other "slight" words or phrases are available; e.g. "this," "these," "in question." If the participle is an honest one, even by the standards of a language with a definite article, it will usually come after the noun in English.

§12. PREPOSITIONAL PHRASES

1. поэтому интеграл, стоящий в правой части тождества (5), аналитически продолжается во всю область

   {thus the integral standing on the right side of the identity (5) is analytically continued to the whole domain}

   thus the integral on the right side of (5) can be analytically continued to the whole domain

2. характеристика, проходящая через точку A, не совпадает с характеристикой проходящей через точку B

   {the characteristic passing through the point A does not coincide with the characteristic passing through the point B}

   the characteristic through A is not the same as the one through B

3. буквой M (снабженной индексами) обозначаются положительные константы

   {by the letter M (equipped with indices) are denoted positive constants}

   the letter M, with subscripts, will denote positive constants

In English a prepositional phrase can be used equally well as an adjective or as an adverb. For example, in the sentence "the coat on the wall was made in Germany" the phrase "on the wall" is adjectival and the phrase "in Germany" is adverbial. In Russian a prepositional phrase is much more likely to be adverbial, usually as the result of insertion of a participle; thus a Russian would say "the coat hanging on the wall . . . ." Consequently it is wise, and at times almost mandatory, to omit certain Russian participles in translation. The three examples given above are representative of countless others. (See also "participles as slight words").

§13. REPETITION OF WORDS

1. предположим, что $F * G = H$, где композиция $*$ определена по формуле $F * G = RS$, причем $R = TV$

   {we assume that $F * G = H$, where the operation $*$ is defined by $F * G = RS$, where $R = TV$}

   we assume that $F * G = H$, the operation $*$ being defined by $F * G = RS$, where $R = TV$

2. вытекает существование факторизации $N = N_1 N_2$, где $N_1 N_2$ —инвариантные подгруппы взаимно простых порядков, причем наибольшими П-делителями этих порядков соответственно ν_1, ν_2

   {thus there exists a factorization $N = N_1 N_2$, where N_1 and N_2 are invariant subgroups of mutually prime order, where the largest П-factor of these orders is ν_1, ν_2, respectively}

   . . . of mutually prime order, the largest П-factor being . . .

There are two complementary mistakes involving repetition of words; in the first one, the same Russian word is used twice in exactly the same setting but the translator uses two different words in English, perhaps from a false notion that the style is thereby improved; in the second, the Russian uses two different words, in different grammatical settings, but the translator, for any one of various insufficient reasons, uses the same word twice in English.

Thus it is highly objectionable to translate область G . . . а область H . . . by "the domain G . . . but the region H . . ."; and

on the other hand it may be necessary to find two ways of translating где and причем. Sometimes this is difficult, but usually
either the где or the причем can be translated by a participle.

§14. SENTENCE CONNECTION

1. эти понятия, вообще говоря, разные. Так,
   например, в кольце матриц, . . .

   {these concepts are in general, distinct. Thus, for
   example, in the ring of matrices, . . . }

   Omit the "thus".

2. отсюда вытекает, что . . .

   {from this it follows that . . . }

   Omit "from this".

In any rational discourse, every sentence must have some
logical connection with its predecessor. But the connection may
be indicated either explicitly, by a particular word like "thus" or
"but," or else implicitly; i.e., some words near the beginning of
the second sentence remind the reader of words near the end of
the first. Since the explicit method is commoner in Russian than
in English, the translator has a golden opportunity for "translation by omission."

§15. SEPARATION OF SYMBOLS

1. при $t \longrightarrow \infty$, $|u(t, x) - a| \longrightarrow 0$ равномерно для
   всех x

   {for $t \longrightarrow \infty$, $|u(t, x) - a| \longrightarrow 0$ uniformly for all x}

   for $t \longrightarrow \infty$ we have $|u(t, x) - a| \longrightarrow 0$ uniformly
   in x

2. проведем через точку Nn $(n-1)$-мерных
   плоскостей $y_i = C$, $i = 1, 2, \cdots n \cdots$

   {we draw through the point Nn $(n-1)$-dimensional
   planes . . . }

   through the point N we draw the n hyperplanes
   $y_1 = C$ of dimension $(n - 1)$ . . .

If two expressions, each consisting entirely of mathematical symbols, occur in immediate juxtaposition, it is natural for the reader to assume that they form one expression, or at least that they are syntactically parallel. If this is not the case, such expressions should be separated by words. A sentence like "if P, Q" (meaning "if P, then Q") is perhaps acceptable, but only because the "then" clause is very short; in the first of the two examples given above (in general, the difficulty is more insidious in longer sentences) the reader will mentally begin "if $t \to \infty$ and $|u(t, x) - a| \to 0 \ldots$" and will then receive a mental jolt. Even in mathematics, where reading proceeds very slowly, a style is not good if it compels the reader to readjust his first impression of the syntax.

In the second example the trouble is even more pronounced; the three expressions N, n and $(n - 1)$ should certainly be separated by words. As they stand, the reader will first feel that they are intended for a product and will then, with the next few words, be jerked up in a very unpleasant fashion.

§16. SEPARATION OF VERB AND OBJECT

1. выделим в прямом разложении (19) слагаемое...

    {we select in the direct decomposition (19) a summand ...}

    in the direct decomposition (19) we select a summand ...

2. напоминаем, что мы не отличаем в записи матрицы

    {we recall that we do not distinguish in our notation matrices ...}

    we recall that in our notation we do not distinguish matrices

3. следует, что в течение процесса в этом слове находится точно один челнок

    {it follows that in the course of the process in this word there is always exactly one shuttle}

    it follows that in the course of the process there is always one shuttle in this word

Separation of verb and object by a prepositional phrase is extremely common in Russian; but in English it is much rarer, the feature of decisive importance being the relative length of the phrase and the object: compare "he read with great interest the book he had received from his daughter," which is quite acceptable, with "he read with great interest the book," which is impossible.

The best cure is usually to put the prepositional phrase in front of the subject, either at the beginning of the sentence (example 1) or, in a "that" clause (example 2), immediately after the "that." Example 3 illustrates the amusing fact that, although English is much more likely than Russian to put a single prepositional phrase up in front in this way, it cannot put two of them there (unless one of them merely modifies the other), whereas a Russian writer is quite free to do so if he wishes.

§17. SINGULARS AND PLURALS

1. эти системы имеют как угодно медленно растущие множители

   {these systems have arbitrarily slowly growing factors}

   each of these systems has a factor of arbitrarily slow growth

2. локализуемость следует из постулатов Маклейна, о единичных сомножителях и ослабленного постулата Мальцева

   {the localizability follows from the postulates of MacLane, on unit factors and the weakened postulate of Mal'cev}

   the localizability follows from the MacLane postulate, the unit-factor postulate, and the weakened Mal'cev postulate

3. пусть p^a, $a > 0$, —любая и q^b, $b > 0$, —наивысшая степени различных или совпадающих простых чисел p и q, делящие соответственно g и h

{let p^a, $a > 0$ be an arbitrary and q^b, $b > 0$, be the highest powers of distinct or identical prime numbers p and q dividing g and h respectively}

let p^a, $a > 0$, be an arbitrary power of p dividing g, and let q, $b > 0$ be the highest power of q which divides h, where p and q are primes, not necessarily distinct

It is a general rule, at least in English, that singulars are clearer than plurals. Consider the sentence: "when husbands are discussing problems with their wives, they almost never know whether they understand them." Here everything is ambigious, including even whether a husband has more than one wife. How much clearer it is to say, for example: "when a husband is discussing a problem with his wife, she almost never knows whether he understands her."

Thus in a phrase like "these systems have factors of arbitrarily slow growth" (example 1) it is not clear whether each system has more than one factor; and the phrase "the postulates of Mac-Lane and Mal'cev" leaves the reader uncertain whether MacLane and Mal'cev share several postulates, or each has several of his own, or MacLane has one and Mal'cev several, and so forth. How much better to use the singular, with no false fear of repetition of words: "the postulate of MacLane and the postulate of Mal'cev."

The desirability of translating in the singular is increased by the following feature of Russian syntax.

In English we may say: "he sent me a blue book and a black book" or "he sent me a blue and a black book", but not (as regularly in Russian) "he sent me a blue and a black books" (послал мне синюю и черную книги). Without a clear understanding of this principle, a translator is likely to be helpless in the face of a sentence like example 3, where любая and наивысшая are singular adjectives modifying the plural noun степени.

§18. SLIGHT WORDS

1. требуя лишь выполнения условий ортогональности
   матрицы A, что, как известно, всегда можно
   сделать

{requiring only fulfilment of the conditions of orthog-
onality of the matrix A, which, as is known, can
always be done}

requiring only, as is of course possible, that A be
orthogonal

2. таким образом, легко убедиться, пользуясь
этими леммами, что ...

{in this manner, it is easy to convince ourselves,
using these lemmas that ... }

so from these lemmas it is easy to see that ...

3. изложенным методом можно решать ряд прак-
тически важных задач

this method enables us to solve several problems
of practical importance

4. классы A, B тривиальны или нетривиальны
одновременно

the classes A and B are either both trivial or
both nontrivial

5. при этом минимальный радиус этих кругов не
меньше чем r/n

{in this connection (in addition, here, furthermore)
the minimal radius of these disks is not less than
r/n }

the minimal radius of these disks is ...

6. помощью лемм 1 и 2 получаем следующую
теорему

{with the help of lemmas 1 and 2, we obtain the
following theorem}

from lemmas 1 and 2 we obtain the following theorem

7. пользуясь приведенными выше результатами
нетрудно доказать, что ...

{using the results introduced above it is not difficult
to prove that ... }

from these results it is easy to show that ...

Every language contains many words or expressions that were
originally meaningful but have been used so often that the reader
is scarcely aware of their presence. If translated literally (and
very often it is hard to translate them in any other way) they are
already overtranslated. A good example is the Russian phrase
как известно, often translated by "as is known" or (usually
somewhat better) by "as is well known." But in many cases the
author is referring to a mathematical fact which is indeed sufficiently well known that to call it so in English becomes absurd
and we must use some such phrase as "of course" or "naturally,"
or "obviously" or some other "slight" English word, or perhaps
even nothing at all.

Other examples are: то, which is slighter than the English
"therefore" or "then"; в связи с этим, slighter than "in connection with this result"; таким образом, usually much slighter
than "in such a manner," ряд, often much slighter than "series";
действительно, slighter than "actually," убедиться, considerably slighter than "to convince oneself"; одновременно, slighter
than "simultaneously"; в самом деле, slighter than "in actual
fact." In example 5 the slight force of при этом, often overtranslated, is probably carried sufficiently well by the English word
"these."

§19. SYMBOLS AS SYNTAX CARRIERS

1. так как рассматриваемые $n < 2p^2 - 7p + 7$, то ...

   {since the considered $n < 2p^2 - 7p + 7$, then ... }

   since the values of n in question are all less than
   $2p^2 - 7p + 7$, therefore ...

2. оператор, заданный на $u \in C^2$, удовлетворяющих
   $u(0) = u(1) = 0$

   {an operator defined on $u \in C^2$ satisfying $u(0) =
   u(1) = 0 ... $}

   an operator defined for functions u with $u \in C^2$
   and $u(0) = u(0) = 0$

For several reasons a Russian writer can assign to his mathematical symbols a much greater syntactical activity than is possible in English. The chief reason is that in Russian a modifying participle can indicate the case of the noun represented by a set of symbols. Thus in the first example, the participle рассматриваемые is nominative plural and must therefore modify the plural noun implied by the symbol n, a fact which in turn implies that the symbol $<$ must be the main verb of the sentence. But choreography of this sort is scarcely possible in English.

In the second example, the participle удовлетворяющих is in the prepositional case and therefore cannot modify anything in the preceding part of the sentence except the symbol u; and again some readjustment is necessary in English.

§20. SYMBOLS IN THE GENITIVE CASE

1. элементы пространства W различны

   {the elements of the space W are distinct}

   the elements of W are distinct

2. получим пространство W; свойства элементов W очевидны

   we obtain the space W; the properties of the elements of W are obvious

3. каждая непустая порция $[a, b]$ имеет положительную меру

   every non-empty part of $[a, b]$ has positive measure

   or: every non-empty part $[a, b]$ has positive measure?

4. для того, чтобы некоторая подполугруппа S была изоморфна

   in order that some subsemigroup S may be isomorphic ...

   or: some subsemigroup of S ...?

Phrases like "the elements of the set S" or "the points of the space W" are very common, but if the set, or space, group, field etc. has been mentioned just before, it is more natural in

English to say "the elements of S," "the points of W" etc.

In this respect English has the advantage over Russian, since a mathematical symbol can be preceded by an "of" but cannot be modified by a case-ending. Thus in the first example the word пространства merely indicates that the symbol W is in the genitive case, a task very well performed by the English word "of."

But the Russian writers are not consistent; sometimes they too omit пространства (or группы, поля or the like) with results that can be surprisingly troublesome. In example 2, W is in turn accusative and genitive; in 3 it is hard to say at first glance whether $[a, b]$ is genitive or nominative; and finally, in example 4, it may even require careful study of the entire article to determine whether S is nominative or genitive, although the decision will have an essential effect on the meaning. Moreover, it is quite impossible for the translator to take refuge, as is so often done with other ambiguous passages, in a mere reproduction of the ambiguity in English.

§21. VERBAL ADJECTIVES (PASSIVE)

1. оператор A называется ядерным, если он представим в виде ...

   {the operator A is called a kernel operator if we represent it in the form ... }

   ... if it can be represented in the form ...

2. для этих уравнений применим принцип максимума

   {for these equations we shall apply the maximum principle}

   for these equations the maximum principle is applicable

The present passive participle of an imperfective verb, e.g. представлять (to represent), is

    представляемый,   представляемая,   представляемое,

and for a perfective verb, e.g. представить, the corresponding formation occurs very frequently in mathematical literature in the shortened predicative forms

    представим,   представима,   представимо.

Nevertheless the grammars assert that perfective verbs have no present passive participles.

The reason for this assertion is as follows. In the first place, the perfective aspect is considered as having no present tense of any kind; e.g. the perfective представлю is a future (I shall represent), so that представим may be called a future passive participle, with some such meaning as "about to be represented." However, the grammars do not call it a participle at all, but rather a "verbal adjective," since its actual meaning is almost never "about to be represented" but "such as can be represented" or "such as ought to be represented." Similarly, in classical Latin the future passive participle "amandus," seldom means "such as will be loved" but rather "such as ought to be loved," and is therefore not called a participle, but a gerundive (or verbal adjective).

With this situation clearly in mind, translators will be able to avoid the common mistake of confusing the verbal adjective представим (representable) with the first person plural indicative представим (we shall represent).

In example 1, the translation "if we represent it . . ." is simply a blunder, since он cannot be accusative, and in the second example it is probable that a Russian reader will automatically take представим as a verbal adjective, even though grammatically it could be taken as a first person indicative.

Part Two

RUSSIAN WORDS AND PHRASES

§1. большой

1. о представлении больших чисел (бо́льших чисел)

   on the representation of large numbers (of larger numbers)

2. с бо́льшим числом

   with a greater number

3. с показателем на единицу большим, чем ...

   with exponent greater by unity than ...

The comparative degree (greater) of the adjective большой (great) usually occurs in the predicate in the uninflected form больше. But an inflected form is sometimes used, especially in the genitive and instrumental cases; e.g. больших and большим. In speaking, the accent on these comparative forms falls on the first syllable, in contrast to the positive forms, which are otherwise indistinguishable from them. Thus the Russian texts customarily print an accent on the comparative forms except where it is clear from the context (example 3) that the comparative is intended.

§2. должно

1. нетрудно убедиться, что найдется такое натуральное число i. Но тогда C_{i+1} должно содержить точку x.

   {it is easy to show that there exists such a positive integer i. But then C_{i+1} should contain the point x.}

   But C_{i+1} must contain the point x.

Although there are many places where должно should be translated by "should," it must sometimes be translated by "must." In the example, the translation "then C_{i+1} should contain the point x" suggests (falsely) that it ought to but in fact does not.

22

§3. если же

1. если k нечетно, то и $k + 2m$ нечетно, если же
   k четно, то y—не квадрат

   if k is odd, then $k + 2m$ is also odd; but if k is
   even, then y is not a perfect square

2. предположим сначала, что $a \geq 0$; имеем ...;
   если же $a < 0$, то ...

   we first assume $a \geq 0$, when we have ...; but if
   $a < 0$, then ...

In a mathematical passage the best translation of если же
is always "but if"; at least, after examining many cases, the
writer has never found a counterexample. The particle же can be
translated in many other ways in other contexts, but not after
если.

§4. замена

1. с заменой k на m

   {with the substitution of k for m}

   with the replacement of k by m or: with the
   substitution of m for k

Translators sometimes confuse the two words "substitution"
and "replacement." The English word "change" is ambiguous,
as in Ben Jonson's song "... But might I of Jove's nectar sup, I
would not change for thine"; but there is no ambiguity about the
corresponding Russian word замена. Thus замена синей книги
черной (exchange of a blue book for a black book) can mean only
that the speaker originally had a blue book and now he has a black
book. If the translator hastily writes "substitution of a blue book
for a black one", he has made an elementary blunder that makes
nonsense out of any mathematical passage.

§5. и

1. это я и сделал

   {I also did this}

   this is what I did

2. получим sup $k \geq 1$, что и проводит к 5.26

   {we obtain that sup $k \geq 1$, which also leads to 5.26}

   thus sup $k \geq 1$, as needed for 5.26

3. можно брать полиномы того же вида, что и ϕ

   {we may take polynomials of the same form as ϕ
   also is}

   ... of the same form as ϕ

Hilaire Belloc wrote an essay on the subtleties of "and."
The Russian word и is equally subtle but the subtleties are different, so that the translator must sometimes reject the automatic
translation "and" or "also." In example 2 "also" is quite wrong,
since it implies that some other result also leads to 5.26; the
meaning is something like "exactly" or "namely," but either of
these words is an overtranslation. The standard procedure is
shown in example 1; but often it cannot be applied; thus in example 3 nothing seems feasible except to disregard the и altogether.

§6. каково бы ни было

1. каково бы ни было a > 1, можно построить ...

   {whatever $a > 1$ may be, it is possible to construct ...}

   for arbitrary $a > 1$, we can construct ...

If the phrase каково бы ни было, or any of its variants, is
translated in any way other than "for arbitrary ... " or "for
every ...," the result will probably seem clumsy.

§7. ли

1. интересно, сохраняют ли метризуемость произ-
   вольные регулярные отображения

   {it is interesting whether metrizability is preserved
   under arbitrary regular mappings}

   it is an interesting question whether ...

The range of words that can introduce an indirect question is
wider in Russian e.g.; интересно, ... ли ... (it is interesting
whether) than in English.

§8. называть

1. тором T^k называем прямое произведение k
окружностей

   {a torus T^k is called the direct product of k circles}

   the direct product of k circles is called a torus

2. если G ранга 1, то $B(G)$ назовем открытое
множество, которое ...

   {if G is of rank 1, we shall call $B(G)$ an open set
which ...}

   if G is of rank 1, then by $B(G)$ we shall mean an
open set which ...

3. ... главной частью оператора L назовем оператор
L_0... и число $2p$ назовем обобщенным порядком
уравнения

   {... the principal part of the operator L we shall call
the operator L_0 ... and the number $2p$ we shall call
the generalized order of the equation}

   ... L_0 is called the principal part of L, and $2p$ is
the generalized order of the equation

4. будем называть K-циклом Δ-цикл, являющийся
K-множеством

   {we shall call a K-cycle a Δ-cycle if it is a K set}

   a Δ-cycle which is also a K-set will be called a
K-cycle

5. будем называть k-мерные интервалы интервалами
направления

   {we will call k-dimensional intervals intervals of
direction}

   the k-dimensional intervals will be called direction
intervals

Consider the definition "a *torus* T^k is the direct product of
k circumferences (of circles)." Here, as is usual in mathematical
writing in English, the concept to be defined (the definiendum) is

italicized, and the concept in terms of which it is defined (the definiens) is left unitalicized. In the corresponding Russian (see example 1 and 2) the definiendum тором (or in example 2 the symbol $B(G)$ is in the instrumental case (usually unitalicized) and the definiens is in the accusative after the verb называем (or in the nominative with the reflexive verb называется). But many variations are possible, in both English and Russian, with consequent difficulties of translation.

Thus in the Russian all six permutations of the word-order тором называем произведение actually occur (note the variation in word-order in example 3) and the translator must take care not to interchange the roles of definiens and definiendum, since the resulting confusion (as in example 4) will cause acute discomfort in the reader's mind.

In English it is usually desirable to let the verb separate the definiens from the definiendum; a juxtaposition like интервалы интервалами (example 5) is acceptable in Russian (and is in fact quite common), but in English "intervals intervals" is highly objectionable.

§9. некоторый

1. напомним, что о некотором ядре K мы говорим, что оно допускает биортогонализацию в H, если . . .

   {we recall that concerning some kernel K we say that it admits a biorthogonalization in H if . . .}

   we recall that a kernel K is said to admit . . .

2. где p —некоторый параметр

   {where p is some parameter}

   where p is a parameter

3. при этом гомоморфном отображении соотношения между высказываниями будут отображаться некоторыми соотношениями между переменными

   under this homomorphism the relations among the propositions will be mapped onto relations among the variables

The (correct) belief that Russian has no indefinite article has been elevated by some translators into the (false) doctrine that некоторый should never be translated by "a," nor its plural некоторые by the plural of "a," namely nothing at all. The three examples above are given in the hope of undermining this doctrine.

§10. обозначить

1. обозначим ее Γ

   let us call it Γ

2. обозначим еще $f = \max T(x)$

   let us also set $f = \max T(x)$

3. обозначим через S оператор ортогонального проектирования ... ; обозначим далее $P = E - S$

   we denote by S the operator of orthogonal projection ...; and we also set $P = E - S$

The one Russian verb обозначить can do the work of several English verbs: "designate," "denote," "call," "set." Confusion among them leads to some very unidiomatic expressions.

§11. общий

1. два элемента пространства имеют общее расположение, если изображающие их плоскости имеют $(m + 1)$ общих перпендикуляров

   {two elements of the space are in general position if their representative planes have $(m + 1)$ general perpendiculars}

   ... have $(m + 1)$ perpendiculars in common

The Russian word общий can mean either "general" or "common"; occasionally it may be difficult to decide between them.

§12. по

1. разложение по собственным функциям

   an expansion in eigenfunctions

2. разложение функций в евклидовом пространстве
по функциям ϕ_k

{expansion of functions in Euclidean space according to functions ϕ_k}

expansion of a function in Euclidean space in a ϕ_k-series

3. по известной теореме

by a well-known theorem

4. по определению индуктивного предела

by the definition of an inductive limit

5. операторы сравниваются по методу Л. Хермандера

the operators are compared by the Hörmander method

In many cases "according to" is not an acceptable translation for the ubiquitous Russian по. In fact, a good translation is sometimes hard to find. Thus even the common phrase "expansion in a series of functions" (see example 2) can cause trouble.

§13. пока, пока не

1. челнок будет повторять этот цикл, пока не сможет выполнить (2); пока сможет выполнить (2)

the shuttle will repeat this cycle until it can satisfy (2); until it cannot satisfy (2)

The Russian word пока means "as long as", and in spite of an apparently widespread opinion it does not mean "until." Consequently пока не (often with intervening words) means "as long as ... not", which is usually best translated by "until"; thus "he waited as long as I did not come" is much less idiomatic in English than "he waited until I came." Therefore пока alone, as the negative of пока не, can be translated, not only by "as long as," but also by "until ... not." Compare "he waited as long as he could" and "he waited until he could not wait any longer." If the не, is widely separated from the пока, translators who are in a hurry sometimes translate пока ... не by "until ... not," with consequent shipwreck of the sense.

§14. пункт

1, доказательство разобьем на несколько пунктов

we shall give the proof under several headings

The Russian word пункт means an "item," "heading" or "subsection," usually numbered; параграф means "section"; the Russian word for "paragraph" is абзац.

§15. работа

1. следует из общих теорем работ [17], [18]

{it follows from the general theorems of the works [17], [18]}

it follows from the general theorems of [17], [18]

2. в работе

{in the work}

in the present article

When работа refers to a definite book or article, the translation "work" is sometimes unidiomatic; работа should then be translated by "book" or "article," depending on which of the two it actually is; but often it can simply be omitted.

§16. тот или иной

1. этот пример наводит на мысль изучать распределение тех или иных функционалов

{this example suggests that we should study the distribution of these or other functionals}

... of the various functionals

The Russian phrase тот или иной does not mean "this or another" but rather "one or another," "some or other," and can usually be translated by "various."

§17. уже

1. на плоскости это утверждение справедливо. Уже
   на поверхности прямого кругового конуса это
   может быть не так

   on the plane this statement is correct. But even on
   the surface of a right circular cone there may be
   exceptions

2. остальная часть доказательства проводится уже
   более или менее просто

   the rest of the proof is now more or less straight-
   forward

3. все эти подгруппы сопряжены с F уже с
   помощью элемента из G

   each of these subgroups is seen to be conjugate
   to F under transformation by an element in G

4. результат уже не получается

   the result can no longer be obtained

In Russian, as in German and elsewhere, the word for
"already" often causes trouble, since care must be taken not to
overtranslate it. The first two examples show that words like
"even," or "now" are sometimes available, but the third example
offers difficulty; the meaning is that even the subgroup G is
large enough to provide elements that will transform the given
subgroups into F; but in this setting the English word "already"
is unidiomatic, and it is very hard to find another word or phrase
short enough not to be clumsy; Admittedly, something is lost by
omitting the уже. In a negative sentence (example 4), "already"
... not" usually becomes "no longer" in English.

Part Three

ENGLISH WORDS AND PHRASES

§1. "a" or "the"?

1. пусть F—Фраттини-подгруппа группы G

   {let F be a Frattini subgroup of G}

   let F be the Frattini subgroup of G

2. совокупность всех элементов коммутативной группы G, порядок которых есть степень p, называется примарной компонентой, или p-компонентой группы G

   the set of all those elements of an abelian group G whose orders are powers of a given prime p is called a primary component, or the p-component, of G

The absence of definite and indefinite articles in Russian often makes it hard to decide whether a word like подгруппа should be translated by "the subgroup," "a subgroup," or simply "subgroup." Consider the first example above. If G has exactly one Frattini subgroup (as in fact it certainly does), we must write "the," but if more than one, then "a." If a translator is not sure which is the case, and is in too big a hurry to find out, he may try something like "let G be a group and H a Frattini subgroup"; but the subterfuge is seldom successful.

§2. and

1. машина обладает некоторой клеткой, конечным числом состояний и всегда находится в одном из них.

   {the machine has a cell, a certain number of states and is always in one of them}

   ... a cell and a certain number of states ...

2. все критерии полиномов наилучшего приближения: Чебышева, Колмогорова, Зуховицкого и Стечкина

{all the criteria for polynomials of best approximation: namely those of Čebyšev, Kolmogorov, Zuhovickiĭ and Stečkin}

Insert "and" before Zuhovickiĭ.

3. все элементы являются пределами произведений элементов вида $\psi^{-1}\phi\psi$, $\psi \in F$, $\lambda \cdot \mu$ —непрерывный гомоморфизм

{all the elements are limits of products of elements of the form $\psi^{-1}\phi\psi$, $\psi \in F$, $\lambda \cdot \mu$ is a continuous homomorphism}

Insert "and" between $\psi \in F$ and $\lambda \cdot \mu$

The commonest reason for unsatisfactory translation of Russian mathematics is failure on the part of the translator to remember that Russian often omits "and" where it is necessary in English; e.g. the usual (though not invariable) Russian way of saying: "let us construct a triangle, a circle and a square" is "let us construct a triangle, a circle, a square."

In example 2 the Russian means that Čebyšev and Kolmogorov have one criterion apiece, and Zuhovickiĭ and Stečkin have one between them; if the latter two authors had one apiece, the и in the Russian would be replaced by a comma.

In a sentence like 3, where the required "and" comes between mathematical symbols (or just before or just after a symbol) translators are particularly likely to omit it, with harsh results.

§3. anomalous use of "if"

1. если в известном способе Литтльвуда уже в первом шаге навязывается избыточный множитель, то неравенство (3) этого недостатка не имеет

{if in the well-known Littlewood method already in the first term there intrudes a redundant factor, then inequality (3) does not have this disadvantage}

in the well-known Littlewood method a redundant factor is introduced even in the first term, but inequality (3) does not have this disadvantage

2. если числа l_k естественно считать равномерно
   ограниченными, то для m_k дело обстоит иначе

   {if the numbers l_k may naturally be taken to be
   uniformly bounded, then the situation is different
   for the m_k}

   although it is natural to make the assumption that
   the l_k are bounded, the case is different with the
   m_k

3. если классический математический анализ
   оперирует с "хорошими" функциями, то теория
   функций действительного переменного изучает
   значительно более общие классы функций

   if classical analysis operates essentially with
   "good" functions, the theory of functions of a real
   variable investigates considerably wider classes of
   functions

Certain languages, including English and Russian, have an idiomatic use of the word "if," in which the sentence "if P, Q" does not mean "if P, then Q" but "P and also Q," with the implication that, in view of the known truth of P, the assertion Q is slightly surprising. Thus Chekhov's description of the island of Sakhalin: если в Александровском округе климат морской, то в Тымовском он континентальный may be translated "if the climate is maritime at Aleksandrovsk, it is continental at Tymovsk." Compare an English sentence like "if his parents were poor, they were honest."

But if the Russian scientists use this construction, it is extremely rare in mathematical English, and a translator should avoid it altogether. If he insists on using it, he must remember that the Russian text may lead him astray. For example, if he translates то by "then," the whole passage is reduced to nonsense.

§4. both

1. но обе функции, входящие в (4), непрерывны, и
   потому обе части (4) равны

{but both the functions in (4) are continuous, and
thus both sides of (4) are equal}

but the functions in (4) are both continuous, and
thus the two sides of (4) are equal

It is a solecism in English to use the word "both," instead of
"the two," in a statement which, usually because of the presence
of some word like "together" or "equal," becomes nonsensical
when applied to one person or thing. Thus "the numbers are both
large" but "the two numbers are equal." There is no such limita-
tion on the Russian word оба.

§5. "can" and "may"

1. следует, что решения могут иметь в D лишь
конечное число нулей

   {it follows that the solution may have only a finite
   number of zeros in D}

   ... can have only a finite number ...
   or ... cannot have more that a finite number of ...

2. если $n = 1$, то мы можем этого требования не
налагать

   {if $n = 1$, we may not impose this condition}

   if $n = 1$, we do not need to impose this condition
   or: we may dispense with this condition

3. если $n = 1$, то мы не можем налагать этого
требования

   {if $n = 1$, we may not impose this condition}

   if $n = 1$, we cannot impose this condition

4. если $n = 1$, то мы не можем не налагать этого
требования

   {if $n = 1$, then we may not fail to impose this condi-
   tion}

   if $n = 1$, this condition cannot be discarded

It is true that in English "may" is sometimes more elegant
than "can"; for example, "we may assume that n is prime."

But "can" is much safer, especially with such words as "not" and "only." "May not" is ambiguous in English, e.g. "he may not come" means either "perhaps he will not come" or "he is not allowed to come"; and in Russian, the corresponding ambiguity is avoided by the word-order (examples 2 and 3). Double negatives, as in example 4, are commoner in Russian than in English.

§6. if and only if

1. R считается реализацией формулы $T = S$ в том и только в том случае, когда ...

   {R is considered to be a realization of the formula $T = S$ in the case and only in the case when ... }

   R is said to be a realization of $T = S$ if and only if ...

In Russian there are many variants for "if and only if"; e.g. тогда и только тогда, когда ... etc., but the phrase does not vary in English.

§7. it

1. это выражение поучительно в том отношении, что оно показывает природу функции $\mu(P)$: она получается из координат точки P применением к ним некоторого нелинейного дифференциального оператора

   {this expression is instructive because it shows the nature of the function $\mu(P)$: it is obtained from the coordinates of the point P by application to it of a nonlinear differential operator}

   ...: this function is obtained ... by application to the expression ...

2. неравенство $f(x) \leq 0$ является следствием системы $f_j(x) \leq 0$; т. е. ему удовлетворяют все ее решения

   {the inequality $f(x) \leq 0$ is a consequence of the system $f_j(x) \leq 0$; i.e. all its solutions satisfy it}

   ...; i.e. all the solutions of the latter satisfy the former

3. из определения функции ϕ непосредственно
   вытекает, что она удовлетворяет условиям

   {from the definition of the function ϕ it follows
   immediately that it satisfies the conditions}

   from the definition it follows at once that ϕ
   satisfies the conditions

4. нетрудно проверить, что можно взять ...

   {it is easy to check that it is possible to take ...}

   it is easy to verify that we may take ...

5. рассмотрим функцию $g(z)$, обладающую следу-
   ющим свойством: точка $z = 0$ является ее
   существенно особой точкой

   {we consider a function $g(z)$ with the property that
   $z = 0$ is its essentially singular point}

   ... $z = 0$ is an essentially singular point

Note the profusion in example 1 of Russian words for "it";
это, оно, она, ним; in English some of them must be translated
by the corresponding nouns. In example 1, if ним is translated by
"it" the reader will naturally assume that the operator is applied
to the function, whereas the gender of ним shows that the operator is applied to the "expression" (and the corresponding remark
applies to the word она). Similarly, in example 2, the gender of
ему and ее cannot be reproduced in English.

But the word "it" can cause trouble in numerous other ways.
For example, a representative subject immediately followed by
"it" as an ordinary pronoun (example 3), or by another representative subject (example 4), makes an unpleasant impression. Also,
the word "its" is tricky. Thus "its singular point" necessarily
implies in English that the function has only one such point, whereas the corresponding Russian ее особая точка (example 5) leaves
this question open.

§8. -ly words

1. совершенно аналогично доказывается

   {entirely analogously it is proved that ...}

   in complete analogy with this result, we may prove that ...

2. эти R_M-полупростые кольца автоматически
являются сильно R_M-полупростыми

{these R_M-semisimple rings are automatically
strongly R_M-semisimple}

it follows automatically that these R_M-semisimple
rings are strongly R_M-semisimple

Two successive -ly words, one of them modifying the other,
are objectionable in English and considerable trouble should be
taken to avoid them; the corresponding juxtaposition of adverbs
is fairly common in Russian.

§9. respectively

1. компактная группа Ли тогда и только тогда
нильпотентна (разрешима), если ее конечные
подгруппы нильпотентны (соответственно
разрешимы)

a compact Lie group is nilpotent (solvable) if and
only if all its finite subgroups are nilpotent
(solvable)

The example shows a familiar method of using parentheses
to avoid repetition of phrases. In English "respectively" is seldom inserted in the second parenthesis, and in general the word
"respectively" is used far less often in English than in Russian.

§10. since ..., then

1. так как функции w_i являются решениями этого
уравнения, то разность любых двух из них
можно рассматривать как решения некоторого
линейного уравнения

{since the functions w_i are solutions of this
equation, then the difference of any two of them
may be regarded as the solution of a certain linear
differential equation}

omit the "then"

2. поскольку $z(x, c)$ есть монотонно возрастающая
функция по c при фиксированном значении
$x \in (0, l]$, то $\mu(x) \equiv v(x)$.

{since $z(x, c)$ is a monotonely increasing function
with respect to c for a fixed value of $x \in (0, l]$,
$\mu(x) \equiv v(x)$}

since for fixed $x \in (0, l]$ the function $z(x, c)$ is
monotone increasing in c, it follows that $\mu(x) \equiv v(x)$

The combination "since . . . , then . . ." (так как . . . , то . . .)
is extremely common in mathematical Russian but totally inadmis-
ible in English. When a signpost is needed in English (example 2)
to show where the principal clause begins, the best one is usually
"it follows that," and if this phrase seems too ponderous, the
translator can fall back on the stereotyped "we have."

§11. such that

1. возьмем такую точку на прямой, чтобы . . .

{we take such a point on the line that . . . }

we take a point on the line such that . . .

2. такая последовательность сечений, для
которой . . .

a sequence of sections such that . . .

3. выберем во вмещающем пространстве базис
так, чтобы . . .

we select a basis in the underlying space such
that . . .

The above examples give some of the various possibilities
in Russian for the common mathematical phrase "such that";
there is no corresponding freedom of choice in English.

§12. "the" instead of "this" or "that"

1. носитель преобразования фурье данной функции
называется спектром этой функции

the support of the Fourier transform of a given
function is called the spectrum of the function

2. связь рациональных отображений многообразия
в проективное пространство с классами диви-
зоров на этом многообразии

the connection between the rational mappings of a
variety into a projective space and the classes of
divisors on the variety

In translating from a language that has a definite article (e.g.
English or Greek) into one that does not (e.g. Latin or Russian)
the translator may sometimes have difficulty in deciding whether
to undertranslate the article by omitting it altogether, or to overtranslate it by some such word as "this" or "that"; and converse-
ly, the translator from Latin or Russian into English should be on
the watch for good opportunities to replace "this" or "that" by
"the."

Consider, for example, the two well-known verses of the New
Testament which in the King James version begin "for God so
loved the world ..." (John 3:16) and "for we brought nothing into
this world, ..." (I Timothy 6, 7). In both places the Greek original simply has "the world," but the King James translators, to
whom the Latin text was much more familiar than the Greek, per-
petuated the distinction made by the Vulgate, even though it is
quite unnecessary in English.

The moral for the modern translator is to use "the" for the
Russian этот in those places where the only purpose of этот is
to refer unemphatically to some preceding word (compare "participles as slight words"). Such places are quite common.

§13. whose

1. пусть X —такое пространство, из всякого откры-
того покрытия которого мощности τ можно вы-
делить конечное покрытие

{let X be a space from every open cover of cardinality τ of which a finite cover can be selected}

let X be a space such that from every open cover
of cardinality τ we can select a finite cover

2. сильно позитивный оператор, область определения которого не зависит от t

{a strongly positive operator the domain of definition of which does not depend on t}

... whose domain of definition ...

3. мы получим сумму дробей, числители которых ограничены, а знаменатели имеют следующий вид

{we obtain a sum of fractions the numerators of which are bounded and the denominators of which have the following form}

a sum of fractions with bounded numerators and with denominators of the following form

or: whose numerators are bounded and whose denominators ...

4. разорвем компоненту $\alpha - \beta$ на несколько других, разным из которых и принадлежат A и B

{we break up the component $\alpha - \beta$ into several others, to different ones of which A and B belong}

we break up the component $\alpha - \beta$ into several components in such a way that A and B now belong to different components

It is less objectionable in Russian than in English (example 1) to introduce complicated subordinate clauses by the words "of which," often buried deeply in the middle of the clause. In English, it usually helps (see examples 2 and 3) to substitute "whose" for "of which" (the notion that "whose" can mean only "of whom" is out of date) or to use "with" or some similar construction. Example 4 shows a case (not at all rare) where "whose" is impossible and "of which" is clumsy; in these cases a phrase like "in such a way that ..." is almost mandatory, and almost a cure-all.

Part Four

PREPARATION
OF THE TYPEWRITTEN MANUSCRIPT

The manuscript should be double-spaced with ample margins, on standard-weight $8\frac{1}{2}''$ by $11''$ white unglazed paper; the use of any kind of light-weight paper causes trouble and expense.

The translation should be in such a form that a varitypist (or compositor) who is neither a mathematician nor a linguist can type it without further editing.

Unless other arrangements have been made, the original Russian text should be sent to the publisher along with the translation. Since it may be desirable to cut formulas from the original article and paste them in place in a photocopy ready for printing, the manuscript should be prepared in such a way as to make this pasting process as convenient as possible.

In general, a displayed formula in the text should be left as a space of corresponding size in the manuscript, with its identifying number typed at the right-hand margin.

With formulas and symbols that are not displayed, or are displayed but not numbered, many different procedures are possible. The following has proved satisfactory in practice. If the formula is short and easily written by hand, write it out in full with no identifying mark. Otherwise, indicate its position by a letter of the alphabet A, B, C, ... and write the same letter in the margin of the corresponding position of the Russian page. These are the only marks that should be made on the printed Russian text and they should be so placed as not to interfere with any symbols that the printer may wish to cut out and photograph. Begin again with A at the beginning of each new Russian page; thus, if page 197 of the Russian has three formulas to be indicated in this way, and page 198 has seven, page 199 has five and so on, the typewritten manuscript should be marked 197 A, B, C, 198 A, B, C, D, E, F, G, 199 A, B, C, D, E etc. As indicated here, the new Russian page number should precede every occurrence of the letter A, so that the varitypist can readily compare the typewritten manuscript with the Russian original.

In general, the typists, proofreaders and others will be grateful for any precautions you can take to avoid uncertainty in their minds about just where the counterpart of a given sentence in your translation occurs on the Russian page. For example, be careful to preserve the paragraphing of the original, unless you specifically indicate a desired change.

In the course of translating you will probably find it necessary to correct some errors or misprints in the original. Be sure to call attention to any such change, since otherwise the compositor will simply assume that you have made a slip in copying. For example, if you change $x < y$ to $x \leq y$, make a note in the margin of the manuscript, but do not mark the original Russian copy.

Greek letters occurring in the typewritten manuscript should be underlined in red, and script letters should be circled in blue. As for German letters, they are most easily identified if their Roman equivalents are typed and then underlined in green. If you find it necessary to add or omit any symbols, or sentences, please note this fact in each case.

In the final rereading, at least twenty-four hours after first translating the passage, please check that all sentences are complete and all symbols are clear, and that no sentences, footnotes or other, have been unintentionally left out.